編者話
Foreword

中國人是世界上最懂得吃的民族，數千年來，一直在鑽研飲食藝術，除了創製出各款美味佳餚之外，連平日的主食（南方人一向以米，北方人以麵為主食）也要在烹調上力求創新，務使口味多變，是以才有「粥、粉、麵、飯」的發明。

廣東人一向把米飯視為「正餐」，把粉麵當作「雜糧」，只在不想吃飯時才吃，但單純吃米飯或粉麵，必定會有枯燥之感！

一鍋熱騰騰的粥，一碟香噴噴的飯，又或者一碗滑溜溜的粉麵，只要在用料與做法上花點心思，便能化腐朽為神奇，即使在食慾不振時也能引起食慾。

本書由經驗豐富之烹飪專家馮金陵女士撰寫。作者利用不同材料與配搭，創製出四十六款色香味全、營養豐富的粥粉麵飯食譜，款款烹調容易，對喜愛吃「正餐」或「雜糧」的人士，都是一大喜訊。

The Chinese have developed the art of cooking and eating. To keep abreast of all the latest development in culinary skill, they have created many diverse new fascinating cuisines for centuries. These cuisines include delicacies as well as daily home dishes, like recipes of rice, congee and noodles.

Other than rice (which is the main staple of Southerners), congee and noodles (which are the main staple of Northerners) have been developed to serve as main courses or supplementary courses.

By using simple yet quality ingredients plus a little effort, one can easily prepare a delicious and mouthwatering bowl of piping hot rice, congee or noodles.

In this book featuring a range of 46 recipes, Ms K. L. Fung is imparting to you her culinary knowledge with easy-to-follow methods in preparing appetizing dishes at home, which can make cooking an enjoyment for you.

粥 粉 麵 飯
Congee, Noodles and Rice

目錄

作者：
馮金陵
美術設計：
陳華樂
出版者：
海濱圖書公司
荃灣德士古道220-248號荃灣工業中心14樓
2408 8801
印刷者：
復興橡皮印刷有限公司
荃灣德士古道220-248號荃灣工業中心14樓
2408 8801
總代理：
世界出版社
荃灣德士古道220-248號荃灣工業中心14樓
2408 8801
門市部：
香港柴灣興華邨第二期安興樓713舖
九龍黃埔花園紅棉苑地下
九龍何文田愛民邨愛民商場地下17舖
九龍樂富商場第一期F10至F11舖
九龍將軍澳景林邨景松樓地下5號舖
九龍深水埗寶熙苑商場6號舖
九龍黃大仙商場三樓S36A舖
九龍黃大仙中心地庫B16號舖
新界沙田禾輋邨商場2樓37A舖
新界沙田瀝源邨瀝源商場CC214舖
新界沙田馬鞍山恒安邨商場321號舖
新界大埔富善邨富善商場一樓F110舖
新界荃灣大窩口邨商場B1舖
新界屯門蝴蝶邨蝴蝶商場C221-C222舖
新界屯門良景邨良景商場206舖
新界元朗朗屏邨商場120-121舖
新加坡總代理：
大眾書局 POPULAR BOOK CO.(PTE) LTD.
Blk 231, Bain Street, Unit 04-59,
Bras Basah Complex, Singapore 180231.
338 2323
馬來西亞總代理：
大眾書局 POPULAR BOOK CO. (M) SDN. BHD.
7 Jalan 3/91A
Taman Shamelin Perkasa
Batu 3 1/2, Jalan Cheras
56100 Kuala Lumpur, Malaysia
Tel:9838269
初版日期：
1991年9月
再版日期：
1996年12月
定價：
HK $ 52.00

三鮮通粉 38
Macaroni With Seafood Combination

龍鳳瀨粉 40
Rice Spaghetti With Goose And Chicken In Soup

鮮茄肉茸燴意粉 42
Spaghetti With Tomato And Minced Pork

焗蝴蝶粉 44
Braised Butterfly Macaroni

麵

羅漢齋炒麵 46
Fried Noodles With Assorted Vegetables

七彩炒烏冬 48
Colourful Japanese Noodles

鮮茄牛肉菠菜麵 50
Spinach Noodles With Tomatoes And Beef

斑球伊麵 52
E-Fu Noodles With Garoupa

豬扒湯麵 54
Noodles With Pork Chops In Soup

雙鮮烏冬麵 56
Japanese Noodles With Seafood In Soup

上海炒粗麵 58
Shanghai-Style Fried Flat Noodles

三絲冷麵 60
Cool Noodles With Shredded Ham,
Cucumber And Carrot

雜錦煲仔麵 62
Assorted Noodles In Pot

火腿蘑菇焗闊條麵 64
Fettuccine With Ham And Mushrooms

鮮蝦雲吞麵 66
Noodles With Fresh Shrimp Wonton In Soup

燒雞絲辮麵 68
Braised Noodles With Roast Chicken Slices

飯

鮮蝦炒紅米飯 70
Fried Red Rice With Shrimps

黃鱔焗糙米飯 72
Braised Coarse Rice With Yellow Eel

香茜荷葉飯 74
Steamed Rice With Parsley Wrapped In
Lotus Leaf

燒鰻魚飯 76
Rice With Braised Eel

焗海鮮飯 78
Baked Seafood Rice

雪菜肉絲泡飯 80
Suit-Nei-Hoong Vegetable And
Shredded Pork With Rice In Soup

生炒咸魚牛肉飯 82
Fried Rice With Salted Fish And Beef

咖喱雞提子飯 84
Rice With Curry Chicken And Raisins

臘味糯米飯 86
Glutinous Rice With Dried Pork And
Liver Sausages

鴛鴦炒飯 88
Fried Rice In Two Colours

章魚蠔豉煲仔飯 90
Rice With Octopus And Dried Oysters
In Earthen Pot

田雞焗飯 92
Braised Rice With Frogs

瑤柱排骨煲仔飯 94
Rice With Conpoys And Spareribs In
Earthen Pot

黃魚豬紅粥

YELLOW CROAKER AND PIG'S BLOOD CONGEE

據本草書籍記載，豬血有解毒的效能，可用於中風、頭眩、痘瘡等病患。現代都市人食之，可解除因空氣污染而吸入體內的塵埃。

材料：

黃花魚	十二両
豬紅	八両
米	半杯
薑絲	一湯匙
芫茜、葱	各兩棵
清水	九杯

調味料：

滾油	一湯匙
鹽	適量

做法：

1. 黃花魚去鱗洗淨，加入薑兩片及葱兩棵隔水蒸熟，取出去骨拆肉。
2. 豬紅洗淨切件，放入滾水內煮至再滾，取出盛乾水份。
3. 米洗淨，用少許鹽、油撈勻待用，芫茜、葱洗淨切粒。
4. 保滾清水，放入米保至滾，改文火煮至濃度適中的粥，放入魚肉，豬紅及調味料，洒上薑絲、芫茜及葱花即可供食。

Ingredients:

1 lb yellow croaker
10 oz pig's blood cakes
1/2 cup rice
1 tbsp shredded ginger
2 sprigs parsley
2 sprigs spring onions
9 cups water

Seasoning:

1 tbsp boiled oil
salt

Method:

1. Scale and wash fish. Steam with 2 slices ginger and 2 sprigs spring onions until cooked. Take out and remove bones.
2. Wash and shred pig's blood cakes. Put in boiling water. When it boils up, remove it and drain.
3. Wash rice. Mix with pinch of salt and oil. Set aside. Wash parsley and spring onion. Dice.
4. Boil water. Add rice and bring to the boil. Then cook over mild heat to right consistency. Put in fish, pig's blood cakes and seasoning. Sprinkle with ginger, parsley and spring onions. Serve.

窩蛋牛肉粥
EGG AND BEEF CONGEE

雞蛋和牛肉含有很豐富的營養，能提供小孩發育時所需要的養份。
這款窩蛋牛肉粥，既易入口，又美味，實為大、小朋友的最佳食品。

材料：

雞蛋	四隻
免治牛肉	八両
葱粒、薑絲	各一湯匙
陳皮	¼個
米粉	半両
米	半杯
清水	九杯

醃料：

生抽	兩湯匙
糖	半茶匙
生粉、蛋白	各一湯匙

調味料：

鹽	適量
麻油、胡椒粉	少許

做法：

1. 米粉放入滾油中炸脆，盛起，放碟上壓碎。
2. 陳皮浸軟，刮瓤切幼粒。
3. 牛肉加入醃料拌勻，放入陳皮再拌勻，用小匙盛起牛肉放在米粉上，沾滿炸米粉，做成牛肉丸。
4. 米洗淨，用鹽、油拌勻醃約三十分鐘。
5. 保滾清水，放入米保至再滾，改文火保至濃度適中的粥，加入調味料，放入牛肉丸保至熟，倒入碗內，打下雞蛋，洒上薑絲及葱花即可進食。

Ingredients:
4 eggs
10 oz minced beef
1 tbsp diced spring onion
1 tbsp shredded ginger
1/4 dried tangerine peel
1 oz rice vermicelli
1/2 cup rice
9 cups water

Marinade:
2 tbsp light soy sauce
1/2 tsp sugar
1 tbsp cornflour
1 tbsp egg white

Seasoning:
salt
sesame oil
pepper

Method:
1. Deep fry rice vermicelli until crispy. Dish up and crush.
2. Soak, clean and dice dried tangerine peel.
3. Mix beef with marinade. Fold in dried tangerine peel. Then spoon out beef onto rice vermicelli. Coat beef with rice vermicelli to make beef balls.
4. Wash rice. Marinate with salt and oil for about 30 minutes.
5. Boil water. Put in rice and boil again. Cook over mild heat to right consistency. Stir in seasoning and beef balls. Simmer until beef is cooked. Pour congee into a bowl. On top put egg and sprinkle with ginger and spring onion. Serve.

富貴粥
WEALTHY CONGEE

「富貴粥」本來是以前的富有人家，將吃剩的飯餸，來煮粥再吃，名為富貴粥，而這裏介紹的「富貴粥」，則利用比較名貴的材料，如鮑魚、雞等，混合粉糰來煮成。

材料：

罐頭鮑魚	一隻
雞胸肉	四両
蝦米	一両
冷飯	一杯
粘米粉	¾杯
芫茜、葱	各兩棵
清水	六杯

雞調味料：

鹽	¼茶匙
生粉	半茶匙
麻油、胡椒粉	少許

粥調味料：

鹽	半茶匙
生抽	一茶匙
麻油	少許

做法：

1. 冷飯加清水一杯，用攪拌機磨碎，倒入大碗內，加入粘米粉及¼茶匙鹽搓成軟粉糰。
2. 蝦米洗淨切碎，加入粉糰內搓勻待用。
3. 鮑魚切片；雞胸肉切片，加調味料拌勻。芫茜、葱切粒。
4. 煲滾清水，用小匙把粉糰放入，煮至全部浮起，加入雞肉、鮑魚及調味料煮至再滾起，洒上芫茜、葱即成。

Ingredients:

1 canned abalone
5 oz chicken breast meat
1 ⅓ oz dried shrimps
1 cup stale rice
¾ cup rice flour
2 sprigs parsley
2 sprigs spring onions
6 cups water

Seasoning for chicken breast meat:
¼ tsp salt
½ tsp cornflour
sesame oil
pepper

Seasoning for congee:
½ tsp salt
1 tsp light soy sauce
sesame oil

Method:

1. Puree rice with 1 cup water in a mixer. Pour into a large bowl. Add rice flour and ¼ tsp salt. Knead into a soft dough.
2. Wash and finely chop dried shrimps. Mix well with dough and set aside.
3. Slice abalone. Shred and mix chicken breast meat with seasoning. Dice parsley and spring onions.
4. Boil water. Put in dough with a small spoon. When they all float, add in chicken breast meat, abalone and seasoning. Bring to the boil. Sprinkle with parsley and spring onions. Serve hot.

鮮蜆肉粥
FRESH CLAM MEAT CONGEE

蜆買回來後，要用清水浸兩、三個鐘頭，使去除泥味及內裏藏着的泥沙，同時亦可防止蜆肉變味。假如是連殼炒以供食用者，必須要將外殼擦洗乾淨。

材料：

蜆	一斤
薑	兩片
薑絲	一湯匙
葱	兩棵
米	半杯
清水	九杯

調味料：

鹽	適量
蔴油、胡椒粉	少許

做法：

1. 蜆以鹽水浸四小時，使其吐沙，洗淨抹乾待用。
2. 米洗淨，用少許鹽、油拌勻醃約半小時。
3. 葱洗淨切粒。
4. 保滾清水，加入米、薑片保至再滾，改文火保至濃度適中的粥，放入蜆，加蓋滾至蜆殼張開，下調味料，再洒上薑絲及葱花即成。

Ingredients:

1 ⅓ lb clams
2 slices ginger
1 tbsp shredded ginger
2 sprigs spring onion
1/2 cup rice
9 cups water

Seasoning:

salt
sesame oil
pepper

Method:

1. Soak clams in salted water for 4 hours in order to make them spit out sand. Then wash, pat dry and set aside.
2. Wash and marinate rice with pinch of salt and oil for about 1/2 hour.
3. Wash and dice spring onions.
4. Boil water. Add rice and ginger. Bring to the boil. Cook over mild heat to right consistency. Add clams. Cover and simmer until clam shells open. Stir in seasoning. Sprinkle with shredded gringer and spring onions. Serve.

皮蛋瘦肉粥

CONGEE WITH PRESERVED EGG AND PORK

腸胃消化不好者，不宜吃太稀而米粒未糊化的粥。可將粥煮至軟滑稠濃，細嚼後再吞，如此唾液中的澱粉酶方可將澱粉完全分解，易助消化。

材料：

皮蛋	兩隻
豬肉、排骨	各八兩
薑	兩片
芫茜、葱	各兩棵
米	半杯
清水	九杯

醃料：

紹酒、鹽	各一茶匙

調味料：

鹽	適量

做法：

1. 排骨原塊放入滾水內煮五分鐘，取出洗淨，放入保湯袋內。
2. 瘦肉洗淨，加醃料醃四小時（醃過夜更好）。
3. 皮蛋去殼洗淨，一開六件。芫茜、葱洗淨切粒。
4. 煲滾清水，放入米、瘦肉、排骨及薑片煲至再滾，改文火煲一小時半，取出瘦肉切小片，排骨取出不要。
5. 將瘦肉片放回粥內，加入皮蛋再煮五分鐘，下調味料，洒上芫茜、葱即可進食。

Ingredients:
2 preserved eggs
10 oz lean pork
10 oz spareribs
2 slices ginger
2 sprigs parsley
2 sprigs spring onions
$\frac{1}{2}$ cup rice
9 cups water

Marinade:
1 tsp Shaoxing wine
1 tsp salt

Seasoning:
salt

Method:
1. Parboil spareribs for 5 minutes. Remove and rinse. Put in cloth bag for making soup.
2. Wash and marinate pork for 4 hours.
3. Shell and wash preserved eggs. Each cut into 6 pieces. Wash parsley and spring onions. Dice.
4. Boil water. Put in rice, pork, spareribs and ginger. Bring to the boil. Then cook over mild heat for 1 $\frac{1}{2}$ hour. Remove pork and shred thinly. Discard spareribs.
5. Return pork to congee. Stir in preserved eggs. Cook for another 5 minutes. Add seasoning. Sprinkle with parsley and spring onions. Serve hot.

粟米雞茸粥
CORN WITH MINCED CHICKEN CONGEE

要雞茸軟滑，不會黏在一塊，秘訣是將雞茸剁爛，加調味料後，再加水將雞茸開稀，使成糊狀，注意加水時要不斷用筷子攪勻。

材料：

粟米粒	一杯
雞肉	四両
米	¾杯
芫茜	兩棵
清水	十杯

醃料：

生抽、生粉	各一茶匙
鹽	半茶匙
清水、油	各一湯匙

調味料：

滾油	一湯匙
鹽	適量

做法：

1. 米洗淨，用少許鹽、油拌勻。
2. 雞肉剁碎，加入醃料拌勻。
3. 煲滾清水，放入米煮至再滾，改文火煮至濃度適中的粥，放入粟米、雞茸煮至再滾，加入調味料及芫茜即可進食。

Ingredients:
1 cup corn
5 oz chicken meat
3/4 cup rice
2 sprigs parsley
10 cups water

Marinade:
1 tsp light soy sauce
1 tsp cornflour
1/2 tsp salt
1 tbsp water
1 tbsp oil

Seasoning:
1 tbsp boiled oil
salt

Method:
1. Wash rice. Mix with pinch of salt and oil.
2. Mince chicken meat. Marinate and set aside.
3. Boil water. Put in rice and bring to the boil. Cook over mild heat to right consistency. Add corn and minced chicken. When it boils up, stir in seasoning and parsley. Serve hot.

柴魚花生粥
CHAI-YU AND PEANUT CONGEE

柴魚可在雜貨店或海味舖買到，選購時要揀肉身白淨、鮮色者，假如已變深啡色便表示不新鮮。柴魚之處理方法甚爲簡單，只要用清水浸軟，撕成一條條，便可放在粥內焗之。

材料：

柴魚、花生	各二両
瘦排骨	八両
葱	兩棵
米	半杯
清水	九杯

調味料：

鹽	適量

做法：

1. 花生用清水浸兩小時，隔去水份。
2. 米用鹽、油拌勻，醃約三十分鐘，葱洗淨切粒。
3. 柴魚剪成小片，放入白鑊內炒片刻，取出洗淨待用。
4. 排骨放入滾水內煮五分鐘，取出洗淨，放入布袋內。
5. 煮滾清水，將全部材料放入保至滾，改文火保約兩小時，加入調味料，食時洒上葱花即成。

Ingredients:

3 oz dried fish (Chai-yu)
3 oz peanuts (shells removed)
10 oz skinny spareribs
2 sprigs spring onions
1/2 cup rice
9 cups water

Seasoning:

salt

Method:

1. Soak peanuts for 2 hours. Drain.
2. Marinate rice with salt and oil for about 30 minutes. Wash and dice spring onions.
3. Scissor Chai-yu into thin shreds. Fry in a dried wok for a while. Remove, wash and set aside.
4. Parboil spareribs for 5 minutes. Remove, wash and place in a muslin bag.
5. Boil water. Put in all ingredients and bring to the boil. Cook over mild heat for about 2 hours. Add seasoning. Sprinkle with spring onions. Serve.

韮菜腰膶粥

CONGEE WITH LEEK, PIG'S LOIN AND LIVER

豬腰買回來後，要挑去白筋，否則會有腥味。然後浸水。要腰膶爽口，可用一茶匙白醋，浸十分鐘，再用清水將醋洗淨，然後用生粉醃之，腰膶會更爽口。

材料：

豬腰	三個
豬膶	六兩
陳皮	¼個
薑絲	一湯匙
韮菜	二兩
米	半杯
清水	九杯

醃料：

洋醋	一茶匙

調味料：

鹽	適量
油、生抽	各一湯匙
胡椒粉	一茶匙

做法：

1. 豬膶洗淨切薄片，加醃料醃十五分鐘。
2. 豬腰切開兩邊，切去白筋，加入醃料醃三十分鐘（中途換水數次）。
3. 陳皮浸軟刮瓢，米洗淨，用少許鹽、油拌勻待用。韮菜切粒。
4. 保滾清水，加入米及陳皮保至再滾，改文火保至濃度適中的粥，加適量鹽調味。
5. 將豬膶、豬腰放入滾水中，灼至半熟撈起，放入粥內保至熟，熄火。
6. 拌勻調味料，倒入粥內，洒上薑絲及韮菜拌勻即成。

Ingredients:
3 pigs' loins
8 oz pig's liver
1/4 dried tangerine peel
1 tbsp shredded ginger
3 oz leek
1/2 cup rice
9 cups water

Marinade:
1 tsp white vinegar

Seasoning:
salt
1 tbsp oil
1 tbsp light soy sauce
1 tsp pepper

Method:
1. Wash and thinly slice pig's liver. Marinate for 15 minutes.
2. Halve pigs' loins. Cut away white tendon and marinate for 30 minutes.
3. Soak and clean dried tangerine peel. Wash rice, mix with pinch of salt and oil, then set aside. Dice leek.
4. Boil water. Add rice and dried tangerine peel. Bring to the boil. Cook over mild heat to right consistency. Season with salt.
5. Parboil liver and loin until halfway done. Transfer to congee and simmer until cooked. Turn off heat.
6. Mix seasoning ingredients and pour into congee. Fold in ginger and leek. Serve.

潮州粥
CHAOZHOU-STYLE CONGEE

潮州粥與一般粥品不同之處，是米粒與水份很易分開。要保一保靚的潮州粥，必須放很多的水（大約相等於八、九倍米的份量）。先用猛火保滾，再用中火保十五分鐘，然後熄火焗大約半小時，焗至米粒「開花」爲止。

材料：

蠔仔	八両
冬菇	四隻
免治豬肉	二両
米	¾ 杯
滾水	十杯

蠔仔調味料：

鹽	¼ 茶匙
薑汁、酒	各一湯匙
生粉	一茶匙

冬菇調味料：

糖、油	各一茶匙

豬肉調味料：

生抽	一茶匙
生粉	半茶匙
胡椒粉	少許
清水、油	各一湯匙

做法：

1. 蠔仔洗淨吸乾水份，加入調味料拌勻，放入滾水內灼熟盛起。
2. 冬菇浸軟去蒂，加調味料拌勻蒸十分鐘，取出切粒。
3. 免治豬肉加調味料拌勻，放入六杯滾水內煮熟。
4. 將米及四杯滾水放入保內煮十分鐘，熄火焗十分鐘，加入蠔仔、冬菇、肉碎及適量鹽調味即成。

Ingredients:
10 oz small oysters
4 dried black mushrooms
3 oz minced pork
¾ cup rice
10 cups boiling water

Seasoning for oysters:
¼ tsp salt
1 tbsp ginger sauce
1 tbsp wine
1 tsp cornflour

Seasoning for dried black mushrooms:
1 tsp sugar
1 tsp oil

Seasoning for pork:
1 tsp light soy sauce
½ tsp cornflour
pepper
1 tbsp water
1 tbsp oil

Method:
1. Wash and pat dry oyster. Mix with seasoning. Cook in boiling water. Dish up.
2. Soak, trim and mix mushrooms with seasoning. Steam for 10 minutes. Remove and dice.
3. Mix pork with seasoning. Blanch in 6 cups boiling water until cooked.
4. Cook rice together with 4 cups boiling water in pot for 10 minutes. Turn off heat. Cover for 10 minutes. Then put in oysters, mushrooms and pork. Season with salt. Serve.

生菜鯪魚球粥
LETTUCE AND DACE BALL CONGEE

要鯪魚球入口夠滑，在將魚肉剁爛後，一定要吸乾水份，同時攪魚肉時一定要順着同一方向去攪，否則魚肉易霉。加些少胡椒粉可辟去魚的腥味。

材料：

鯪魚肉	六兩
蝦米	一兩
髮菜	一錢
生菜	一棵
瑤柱	兩粒
米	半杯
薑絲	一湯匙
清水	九杯

醃料：

鹽	¼茶匙
生抽	一茶匙
生粉	一湯匙
麻油、胡椒粉	少許

調味料：

鹽	適量
麻油、胡椒粉	少許

做法：

1. 鯪魚肉剁碎，蝦米用清水浸軟切碎，髮菜洗淨剪碎，加入醃料攪至起膠，做成多個髮菜鯪魚球，排放碟上，大火隔水蒸熟待用。
2. 生菜洗淨，抹乾水份切絲；瑤柱洗淨。
3. 米洗淨，用少許鹽、油拌勻待用。
4. 保滾清水，放入米、瑤柱保至再滾，改文火保約一小時半，放入鯪魚球及調味料，再加入薑絲、生菜絲拌勻即成。

Ingredients:
8 oz dace fillet
1 $\frac{1}{3}$ oz dried shrimps
$\frac{1}{10}$ oz dried sea moss
1 lettuce
2 conpoys
$\frac{1}{2}$ cup rice
1 tbsp shredded ginger
9 cups water

Marinade:
$\frac{1}{4}$ tsp salt
1 tsp light soy sauce
1 tbsp cornflour
pepper
sesame oil

Seasoning:
salt
sesame oil
pepper

Method:
1. Mince dace fillet. Soak and finely chop dried shrimps. Wash and scissor sea moss into pieces. Mix the above ingredients with marinade and blend to sticky consistency. Shape into dace balls. Arrange them on plate and steam until cooked. Set aside.
2. Wash, pat dry and shred lettuce. Wash conpoys.
3. Wash rice. Mix with pinch of salt and oil. Set aside.
4. Boil water. Put in rice and conpoys. Bring to the boil. Then cook over mild heat for about 1 $\frac{1}{2}$ hour. Add dace balls and seasoning. Stir in ginger and lettuce. Serve.

黑糯米紅豆粥

BLACK GLUTINOUS RICE CONGEE WITH RED BEANS

　　黑糯米有補中益氣、健脾固腎的功效，而紅豆則清熱利尿、消腫散血，將兩者混合來煲粥，既新鮮，又夠營養。

材料：

黑糯米	二両
紅豆、片糖	各半斤
椰汁	一杯
陳皮	¼個
清水	九杯

做法：

1. 紅豆、黑糯米洗淨，用清水浸一小時，盛乾水份待用。
2. 陳皮浸軟刮瓤。
3. 保滾清水，放入紅豆、黑糯米、陳皮保至再滾，改慢火保兩小時，加片糖調味，再放入椰汁煮至滾，即可盛起供食。

Ingredients:
3 oz black glutinous rice
3/4 lb red beans
3/4 lb brown sugar
1 cup coconut juice
1/4 dried tangerine peel
9 cups water

Method:
1. Wash red beans and black glutinous rice. Soak for 1 hour. Drain and set aside.
2. Soak and clean dried tangerine peel.
3. Boil water. Put in red beans, black glutinous rice and dried tangerine peel. Bring to the boil. Then cook over low heat for 2 hours. Season with brown sugar. Add coconut juice. When it boils up, serve.

豉椒雞絲炒河

RICE NOODLES WITH SHREDDED CHICKEN IN FERMENTED BEAN SAUCE

要河粉更加爽口，炒之前要將河粉撕開，不致一條條叠在一起。然後燒紅鑊，放下河粉，洒些少水，快手兜炒至河粉熱便可，不用兜得太多，否則河粉易爛。

材料：

河粉	十二両
雞肉	六両
青、紅椒	各一隻
薑絲	半湯匙
豆豉	一湯匙
蒜茸	一茶匙

調味料：

生抽	兩茶匙
糖	¼茶匙
生粉	半茶匙
油	兩湯匙

獻汁料：

上湯	1¼杯
老抽、生抽	各半湯匙
糖	⅛茶匙
生粉	一湯匙

做法：

1. 河粉挑鬆待用，雞肉、青、紅椒全部切絲。
2. 雞絲加調味料拌勻待用。
3. 下油兩湯匙，倒入河粉炒至熱上碟。
4. 燒熱油兩湯匙，放入雞絲炒至將熟，加入青、紅椒絲炒勻，贊酒，兜炒雞絲至熟，放在河粉上。
5. 再下油一湯匙爆香蒜茸、豆豉及薑絲，倒下獻汁料煮滾，淋在河粉上即成。

Ingredients:

1 lb rice noodles
8 oz chicken meat
1 green pepper
1 red chilli
1/2 tbsp shredded ginger
1 tbsp fermented black beans
1 tsp crushed garlic

Seasoning:

2 tsp light soy sauce
1/4 tsp sugar
1/2 tsp cornflour
2 tbsp oil

Sauce:

1 ¼ cups stock
½ tbsp dark soy sauce
½ tbsp light soy sauce
⅛ tsp sugar
1 tbsp cornflour

Method:

1. Make noodles loose and set aside. Shred chicken meat, green pepper and red chilli.
2. Mix chicken meat with seasoning. Set aside.
3. Fry noodles with 2 tbsp oil until heated. Dish up.
4. Fry chicken meat with 2 tbsp oil. When it has just cooked, mix in green pepper and red chilli. Sizzle wine. Fry until chicken meat has thoroughly cooked. Pour contents onto noodles.
5. Saute garlic, black beans and ginger with 1 tbsp oil. Add sauce. Bring to the boil. Pour over noodles. Serve.

沙茶銀針粉

FINGER VERMICELLI IN SATAY PASTE

炒銀針粉與炒河粉一樣，鑊一定要夠熱，炒時洒些少水，令銀針粉吸熱更快，同時不易爛，但記着一定要快手地炒。

材料：

銀針粉	一斤
炸魚（日本炸魚片）	六兩
炸菜絲	一湯匙
菜梗粒	二兩
蝦仁	四兩
紅蘿蔔花	數片

醃料：

鹽、生粉	各¼茶匙
胡椒粉	少許

調味料：

沙茶醬	兩湯匙
老抽	一湯匙
生抽	兩茶匙
鹽	¼茶匙
糖	⅛茶匙

做法：

1. 炸魚切粗絲。
2. 蝦仁洗淨，加醃料拌勻，飛水取出，盛乾水份待用。
3. 下油兩湯匙爆炒菜梗粒、炸魚條、炸菜絲及蝦仁至熟，盛起上碟。
4. 再下油兩湯匙爆香沙茶醬，倒下銀針粉炒熱，將其餘材料及調味料加入，炒至熟透即可供食。

Ingredients:

1 ⅓ lb finger vermicelli
8 oz Japanese fried fish fillet
1 tbsp shredded preserved Sichuan vegetable
3 oz diced vegetable stalk
5 oz shrimps (shells removed)
carrot slices

Marinade:

1/4 tsp salt
1/4 tsp cornflour
pepper

Seasoning:

2 tbsp satay paste
1 tbsp dark soy sauce
2 tsp light soy sauce
1/4 tsp salt
1/8 tsp sugar

Method:

1. Thickly shred fried fish.
2. Wash shrimps. Marinate, parboil, dish up and drain.
3. Add 2 tbsp oil. Saute vegetable stalk, fried fish, preserved Sichuan vegetable and shrimps until heated. Dish up.
4. Saute satay paste with 2 tbsp oil. Add finger vermicelli and fry until heated. Put in rest of ingredients and seasoning. Fry until thoroughly cooked. Serve.

翡翠蝦球炆米

STEWED RICE VERMICELLI WITH BROCCOLI AND SHRIMP BALLS

做炆米時，水份要和米粉配合，使米粉吸收到充份的汁液，米粉才入味，換言之，若上湯放得不夠，米粉便不夠味道。

材料：

米粉、西蘭花	各六両
中蝦	八両
西芹	二両
紅蘿蔔	數片
蒜茸	一茶匙
上湯	一杯

調味料：

鹽	¼茶匙
生粉	半茶匙
胡椒粉	少許

獻汁料：

上湯	¾杯
生抽、生粉	各一茶匙
糖	⅛茶匙

做法：

1. 米粉放入滾水內浸兩分鐘，取出盛乾水份待用。
2. 中蝦去殼去腸，洗淨吸乾水份，切雙飛，加調味料拌勻，泡油盛起。
3. 西芹撕去老根，切片泡油。
4. 西蘭花切成花朵形，用鹽、油、水灼熟。
5. 燒熱兩湯匙油，倒入米粉及上湯，炆煎至兩面微黃色上碟。
6. 下油一湯匙爆香蒜茸，下紅蘿蔔花、西芹、中蝦及西蘭花兜炒，拌勻獻汁料埋獻，放在米粉上即可上桌。

Ingredients:

8 oz rice vermicelli
8 oz broccoli
10 oz medium-sized shrimps
3 oz celery
carrot slices
1 tsp crushed garlic
1 cup stock

Seasoning:

¼ tsp salt
½ tsp cornflour
pepper

Sauce:

¾ cup stock
1 tsp light soy sauce
1 tsp cornflour
⅛ tsp sugar

Method:

1. Soak rice vermicelli in boiling water for 2 minutes. Remove, drain and set aside.
2. Shell, devein, wash and pat dry shrimps. Slit in middle but don't sever. Mix with seasoning. Saute and dish up.
3. Trim, slice and saute celery.
4. Cut broccoli into flowerets. Cook in boiling water together with salt and oil.
5. Heat 2 tbsp oil. Add rice vermicelli and stock. Stew until slightly brown. Dish up.
6. Saute garlic with 1 tbsp oil. Add carrot, celery, shrimps and broccoli. Mix well. Stir in sauce. Pour over rice vermicelli. Serve.

越南金邊粉
VIETNAMESE CAMBODIA NOODLES

金邊粉爲越南食品，比廣東河粉窄而薄，且有透明感，由於薄的關係，多數會被製成湯河，如果做炒河，只須兜兩下便一定要上碟，否則河粉很易爛。

材料：

越南河粉	一斤
扎肉	兩塊
鮮魷魚、靑、紅椒	各一隻
蝦仁	四兩
花生碎	一湯匙
蒜茸	一茶匙

調味料：

上湯	1½杯
生抽	一茶匙
糖	¼茶匙
鹽	⅛茶匙

做法：

1. 河粉飛水，取出瀝乾。
2. 扎肉切條，鮮魷魚切圓圈，蝦仁洗淨，一同泡油盛起。
3. 靑、紅椒切圈。
4. 下油一湯匙爆香蒜茸、靑、紅椒，放入河粉及調味料炒至汁收乾，再放入扎肉、魷魚、蝦仁，兜勻上碟，洒上花生碎即可上桌。

Ingredients:

1 ⅓ lb Vietnamese Cambodia noodles
2 Thai sausages
1 fresh squid
1 green pepper
1 red chilli
5 oz shrimps (shells removed)
1 tbsp crushed peanuts
1 tsp crushed garlic

Seasoning:

1 ½ cups stock
1 tsp light soy sauce
¼ tsp sugar
⅛ tsp salt

Method:

1. Parboil noodles for a while. Remove and drain.
2. Strip sausages. Cut squid into rings. Wash shrimps. All fry in moderate hot oil. Dish up.
3. Cut green pepper and red chilli into rings.
4. Saute garlic, green pepper and red chilli with 1 tbsp oil. Add noodles and seasoning. Fry until sauce is absorbed. Add sausages, squid and shrimps. Mix well and dish up. Sprinkle with crushed peanuts. Serve.

雪菜火鴨絲鴛鴦米

TWO KINDS OF VERMICELLI WITH SUIT-NEI-HOONG VEGETABLE AND ROAST DUCK SLICES

我們到酒樓吃飯，許多時會點一款「雪菜火鴨絲窩米」來吃，有人會將米粉換了粉絲，喜其更爽口幼滑，而這款食譜則是將米粉和粉絲混合一起，讀者不妨試做來吃。

材料：

米粉、雪菜	各四両
粉絲	二両
燒鴨	¼隻
紅椒	一隻
芫茜	兩棵

湯料：

上湯	三杯
清水	1½杯
鹽	¼茶匙

獻汁料：

生抽、生粉	各一茶匙
清水	三湯匙

做法：

1. 米粉、粉絲各用清水浸軟，取出盛乾水份。
2. 雪菜洗淨，用清水浸三十分鐘，洗淨搾乾水份切粒。
3. 燒鴨起肉切絲，紅椒切絲，芫茜切段。
4. 將米粉、粉絲放入滾水內煮滾，取出瀝乾，放入窩內，煮滾湯料，倒入窩中。
5. 下油兩湯匙，加入雪菜炒透，放入燒鴨、紅椒炒勻，埋獻，淋在米粉及粉絲上，洒上芫茜即成。

Ingredients:
5 oz rice vermicelli
5 oz suit-nei-hoong vegetable
3 oz mungbean vermicelli
1/4 roast duck
1 red chilli
2 sprigs parsley

Soup ingredients:
3 cups stock
1 ½ cups water
1/4 tsp salt

Sauce:
1 tsp light soy sauce
1 tsp cornflour
3 tbsp water

Method:
1. Soak rice vermicelli and mungbean vermicelli separately until soft. Remove and drain.
2. Wash and soak vegetable for 30 minutes. Remove, wash and squeeze out excess water. Dice.
3. Remove bones from duck and slice. Shred red chilli. Section parsley.
4. Boil rice vermicelli and mungbean vermicelli for a while. Drain well and place in a tureen. Pour in boiled soup ingredients.
5. Saute vegetable thoroughly with 2 tbsp oil. Mix in duck slices and red chilli. Add sauce. Pour content over rice vermicelli and mungbean vermicelli. Sprinkle with parsley. Serve.

炒貴刁

ES WITH BEEF IN SATAY PASTE

品，其形狀就和河粉一樣，只是在處理上加了一些
味料，吃起來惹味得多。

材料：

牛肉	四両
芥蘭梗	六両
洋葱	半個
白芝麻、沙爹醬	各兩湯匙
河粉	一斤

醃料：

生抽、清水、油	各一湯匙
糖	¼茶匙
生粉	半茶匙

河粉調味料：

生抽	半茶匙
老抽	一湯匙
麻油	少許

芥蘭調味料：

薑汁	一茶匙
糖、鹽	各半茶匙
清水	半杯

獻汁料：

鹽、糖	各半茶匙
生抽	一湯匙
胡椒粉	少許
生粉	一茶匙
清水	半杯

做法：

1. 牛肉切片，加醃料醃十五分鐘，泡嫩油取出，盛乾油份。
2. 芥蘭梗洗淨切段，前後刜十字，下油兩湯匙，放下芥蘭兜炒，倒入芥蘭調味料炒至熟，盛起瀝乾水份。
3. 白芝麻以白鑊炒香，洋葱去皮切絲，下油一湯匙炒至洋葱有香味盛起。
4. 河粉挑鬆，下油三湯匙，放入河粉及調味料炒至熱，放於碟上。
5. 燒熱兩湯匙油爆香沙爹醬，下獻汁料煮滾，牛肉、芥蘭及洋葱回鑊炒勻，放在河粉上，洒上白芝麻即可上桌。

Ingredients:
5 oz beef
8 oz broccoli stem
½ onion
2 tbsp white sesame seeds
2 tbsp satay paste
1 ⅓ lb rice noodles

Marinade:
1 tbsp light soy sauce
1 tbsp water
1 tbsp oil
1/4 tsp sugar
1/2 tsp cornflour

Seasoning for noodles:
1/2 tsp light soy sauce
1 tbsp dark soy sauce
pinch of sesame oil

Seasoning for broccoli:
1 tsp ginger sauce
1/2 tsp sugar
1/2 tsp salt
1/2 cup water

Sauce:
½ tsp salt
½ tsp sugar
1 tbsp light soy sauce
pepper
1 tsp cornflour
½ cup water

Method:

1. Shred beef and marinate for 15 minutes. Saute in warm oil. Remove and drain.
2. Wash and section broccoli. Slit a cross at each end. Fry with 2 tbsp oil. Add seasoning and fry until cooked. Dish up and drain.
3. Fry white sesame seeds in a dried wok until fragrant. Peel and shred onion. Fry onion with 1 tbsp oil until fragrant. Dish up.
4. Make noodles loose. Add 3 tbsp oil. Fry noodles with seasoning until heated. Dish up.
5. Saute satay paste with 2 tbsp oil. Add sauce and bring to the boil. Return beef, broccoli and onion. Mix well. Pour contents onto noodles. Sprinkle with white sesame seeds. Serve.

三鮮通粉

MACARONI WITH SEAFOOD COMBINATION

要通粉煮得爽口不「黏」牙，方法是將水保滾後，放下通粉，但不要煮得太熟，只要剛剛熟便可，略焗一會兒，隔去水份，再用凍水冲去通粉上面的膠質，通粉便會爽口。

材料：

通粉	半磅
中蝦、冬菇	各四隻
帶子	四粒
火腿	一塊
菜薳	四両

帶子調味料：

鹽	1/8 茶匙
生粉	1/4 茶匙

冬菇調味料：

糖	半茶匙
油	一茶匙

湯料：

上湯	兩杯
清水	一杯
鹽	半茶匙
麻油、胡椒粉	少許

做法：

1. 通粉放入滾水內煮至軟身，取出用清水冲凍，瀝乾待用。
2. 中蝦剪去蝦鬚、蝦腳，挑腸，原隻飛水至熟盛起。
3. 帶子吸乾水份，加調味料拌勻，飛水至熟取出。
4. 冬菇浸軟去蒂，加調味料拌勻，隔水蒸十分鐘。菜薳用鹽、油、水灼熟。
5. 保滾湯料，放入通粉至再滾起，加入中蝦、帶子、火腿、冬菇及菜炆煮五分鐘，即可取出供食。

Ingredients:
1/2 lb macaroni
4 medium-sized shrimps
4 dried black mushrooms
4 scallops
1 piece ham
5 oz vegetable stalks

Seasoning for scallops:
1/8 tsp salt
1/4 tsp cornflour

Seasoning for dried black mushrooms:
1/2 tsp sugar
1 tsp oil

Soup ingredients:
2 cups stock
1 cup water
1/2 tsp salt
sesame oil
pepper

Method:
1. Parboil macaroni until soft. Remove and rinse to cool. Drain and set aside.
2. Trim away the antennas of shrimps and remove intestines. Cook in boiling water. Dish up and drain.
3. Pat dry scallops and mix with seasoning. Cook in boiling water. Dish up and drain.
4. Soak and trim mushrooms. Mix with seasoning and steam for 10 minutes. Cook vegetable stalks in boiling water together with salt and oil.
5. Boil soup ingredients. Add macaroni. Bring to the boil. Put in shrimps, scallops, ham, mushrooms and vegetable stalks. Cook for another 5 minutes. Serve.

龍鳳瀨粉
RICE SPAGHETTI WITH GOOSE AND CHICKEN IN SOUP

許多人都喜歡吃瀨粉，因為瀨粉特別爽口幼滑，原來瀨粉在製造時，是在粘米粉中加了澄麵，所以特別爽滑可口。

材料：

瀨粉	一斤
燒鵝、切雞	各六両
雞蛋、青椒	各一隻
銀芽	二両
冬菇	四隻

調味料：

糖	半茶匙
油	一茶匙

湯料：

上湯、清水	各兩杯
生抽	一茶匙
鹽	¼茶匙
胡椒粉	少許

做法：

1. 瀨粉放入滾水內飛水，取出瀝乾，放入湯碗內。
2. 燒鵝、切雞斬件；雞蛋原隻保熟切件。
3. 下油一湯匙猛火兜炒銀芽，盛乾水份。
4. 冬菇浸軟去蒂，加入調味料拌勻，隔水蒸十分鐘。
5. 青椒切絲，下油半湯匙略炒盛起，將所有材料排在瀨粉上。
6. 保滾湯料，淋在材料上即可上桌。

Ingredients:

1 1/3 lb rice spaghetti
8 oz roast goose
8 oz plain chicken
1 egg
1 green pepper
3 oz silver bean sprouts
4 dried black mushrooms

Seasoning:

1/2 tsp sugar
1 tsp oil

Soup ingredients:

2 cups stock
2 cups water
1 tsp light soy sauce
1/4 tsp salt
pepper

Method:

1. Parboil rice spaghetti. Remove, drain and place in a soup bowl.
2. Chop up roast goose and plain chicken. Poach egg and shred.
3. Quickly fry bean sprouts with 1 tbsp oil over high heat. Drain.
4. Soak, trim and mix mushrooms with seasoning. Steam for 10 minutes.
5. Shred green pepper, gently fry with 1/2 tbsp oil and dish up. Arrange all ingredients onto rice spaghetti.
6. Boil soup ingredients. Pour over rice spaghetti. Serve.

鮮茄肉茸燴意粉
SPAGHETTI WITH TOMATO AND MINCED PORK

煮意粉時需放入滾水中出水，再加少許鹽，讓意粉吸收到足夠水份，不會膠着成糊狀，而出水的時間要控制得宜，才可做到軟硬適中，入口「彈牙」兼爽口。

材料：

意大利粉	半磅
番茄、免治豬肉	各四兩
茄膏、青豆	各兩湯匙
洋葱	半個

醃料：

生抽	兩茶匙
生粉	一茶匙
胡椒粉	少許
油	一湯匙

調味料：

茄汁	四湯匙
喼汁、糖	各兩湯匙
鹽	半茶匙
清水	一杯

做法：

1. 意大利粉放入熱水中煮至軟身，用凍水沖淨，瀝乾水份待用。
2. 番茄去皮切粗粒；免治豬肉加醃料拌勻。
3. 洋葱去皮切粒，下油一湯匙爆香洋葱粒盛起。
4. 下油兩湯匙爆茄膏及免治豬肉，加入調味料煮滾，放入意大利粉、番茄、青豆及洋葱粒燴至汁濃，即可盛起上桌。

Ingredients:
1/2 lb spaghetti
5 oz tomato
5 oz minced pork
2 tbsp tomato paste
2 tbsp green peas
1/2 onion

Marinade:
2 tsp light soy sauce
1 tsp cornflour
pepper
1 tbsp oil

Seasoning:
4 tbsp tomato ketchup
2 tbsp worcester sauce
2 tbsp sugar
1/2 tsp salt
1 cup water

Method:
1. Parboil spaghetti until soft. Remove and rinse to cool. Drain and set aside.
2. Skin and cut tomato into cubes. Mix pork with marinade.
3. Peel and dice onion. Saute with 1 tbsp oil. Dish up.
4. Saute tomato paste and pork with 2 tbsp oil. Add seasoning. Bring to the boil. Put in spaghetti, tomato, green peas and onion. Braise until sauce has reduced. Serve.

焗蝴蝶粉
BRAISED BUTTERFLY MACARONI

蝴蝶粉是意大利粉的一種，因外形似蝴蝶而命名。意大利人對吃意粉非常講究，不同形狀的意大利粉會配上不同的醬汁及煮食方法，通常蝴蝶粉會配以沙律醬同食，特別滋味。

材料：

蝴蝶形通粉	半磅
鮮魷魚	一隻
紅蘿蔔、粟米粒	各兩湯匙
玉豆	二兩

醃料：

鹽	1/4 茶匙
生粉	半茶匙
胡椒粉	少許

調味料：

沙律醬、清水	各兩安士
鹽	半茶匙
糖	1/4 茶匙
黑椒粉	少許

做法：

1. 蝴蝶粉放入滾水內煮至軟身，取出瀝乾水份，用一湯匙油拌勻上碟。
2. 鮮魷去衣洗淨，斜剠花紋再切小件，加醃料拌勻飛水。
3. 玉豆撕去頭尾根，斜切粒。紅蘿蔔、粟米飛水。
4. 將調味料拌勻，以慢火煮滾，加入鮮魷、紅蘿蔔、粟米、玉豆兜勻，放在蝴蝶粉上。
5. 預熱焗爐十五分鐘，用高火將蝴蝶粉焗二十分鐘或至微黃色即可盛起供食。

Ingredients:
1/2 lb butterfly macaroni
1 fresh squid
2 tbsp diced carrot
2 tbsp whole kernel corn
3 oz French beans
Marinade:
1/4 tsp salt
1/2 tsp cornflour
pepper
Seasoning:
2 oz salad dressing
2 oz water
1/2 tsp salt
1/4 tsp sugar
grated black pepper
Method:
1. Parboil macaroni until soft. Remove, drain and mix with 1 tbsp oil. Place on a dish.
2. Remove membrane of squid. Make criss cross pattern on surface and cut into small pieces. Marinate and parboil for a while.
3. Top and tail French beans. Then cut diagonally into cubes. Parboil carrot and corn.
4. Boil seasoning over low heat. Put in squid, carrot, corn and French beans. Mix well. Then pour contents onto macaroni.
5. Preheat oven for 15 minutes. Braise macaroni at high power for 20 minutes or braise until slightly brown. Serve.

羅漢齋炒麵
FRIED NOODLES WITH ASSORTED VEGETABLES

炒麵通常用幼蛋麵來炒。要炒麵鬆脆，炒之前須用滾水灼一會，挑鬆麵條，然後倒去滾水，記着不可灼得太久。接着過冷河，將梘水味去除，再瀝乾水份才炒，否則便不會炒得鬆脆。

材料：

幼蛋麵	六両
銀芽、菜薳	各二両
冬菇	四隻
草菇、蘑菇	各六粒
筍肉、紅蘿蔔花	各數片
雲耳、髮菜	各一錢
生筋	兩個
薑	兩片

調味料：

糖、鹽	各¼茶匙
生抽	一湯匙
薑汁	一茶匙
清水	一杯

獻汁料：

上湯	一杯
老抽、麻油	各一茶匙
生粉	一湯匙
蠔油	兩湯匙

做法：

1. 冬菇浸軟去蒂；雲耳浸軟洗淨，飛水；髮菜浸軟洗淨。
2. 生筋放入滾水中灼軟，取出開邊；草菇、蘑菇開邊。
3. 幼麵放入滾水內挑鬆，取出瀝乾水份；燒熱三湯匙油，放入幼麵炒熱上碟。
4. 下油一湯匙炒熟銀芽，盛起；再下三湯匙油爆香薑片、冬菇、草菇、蘑菇及筍肉，下雲耳、髮菜、生筋及調味料，以文火炆十五分鐘至汁將收乾，加入獻汁料、銀芽及紅蘿蔔花炒勻，淋在麵上。
5. 菜薳用鹽、油、水灼熟，放在碟邊即可上桌。

Ingredients:

8 oz egg noodles
3 oz silver bean sprouts
3 oz vegetable stalks
4 dried black mushrooms
6 straw mushrooms
6 button mushrooms
bamboo shoot slices
carrot slices
$\frac{1}{10}$ oz dried black fungus
$\frac{1}{10}$ oz dried sea moss
2 fried gluten puffs
2 slices ginger

Seasoning:

$\frac{1}{4}$ tsp sugar
$\frac{1}{4}$ tsp salt
1 tbsp light soy sauce
1 tsp ginger sauce
1 cup water

Sauce:

1 cup stock
1 tsp dark soy sauce
1 tsp sesame oil
1 tbsp cornflour
2 tbsp oyster sauce

Method:

1. Soak and trim dried black mushrooms. Soak and wash dried black fungus. Drain. Soak and wash sea moss.
2. Parboil gluten puffs until tender. Remove and cut into halves. Halve straw mushrooms and button mushrooms.
3. Rinse noodles in boiling water and make it loose. Remove and drain. Heat 3 tbsp oil. Fry noodles. Place on a dish.
4. Fry bean sprouts with 1 tbsp oil until cooked. Dish up. Add 3 tbsp oil and saute ginger, dried black mushrooms, straw mushrooms, button mushrooms and bamboo shoot. Add black fungus, sea moss, gluten puffs and seasoning. Stew over mild heat for 15 minutes until liquor has dried up. Stir in sauce, bean sprouts and carrot. Pour mixture onto noodles.
5. Cook vegetable stalks in water together with salt and oil. Arrange on the side of plate. Serve.

七彩炒烏冬
COLOURFUL JAPANESE NOODLES

烏冬麵原爲日本食品，近年在香港頗爲盛行，這款「七彩炒烏冬」名符其實，顏色繽紛艷麗，看着已令人垂涎三尺。

材料：

烏冬麵	兩包
日本魚片	一條
洋葱	半個
青、紅椒	各一隻
肉絲	三兩
雞蛋	兩隻
炒香白芝蔴	一湯匙

醃料：

生抽	兩茶匙
糖	¼茶匙
生粉	半茶匙
油	一湯匙

雞蛋調味料：

鹽	¼茶匙
胡椒粉	少許
生粉	半茶匙
清水	一湯匙

麵調味料：

鹽、糖	各¼茶匙
生抽	兩茶匙
薑汁	一湯匙
蔴油、胡椒粉	少許
清水	三湯匙

做法：

1. 魚片切片，洋葱、青、紅椒切絲。
2. 肉絲加醃料拌勻，雞蛋加調味料拌勻，煎成蛋皮切絲。
3. 烏冬麵挑鬆，燒熱油兩湯匙爆香洋葱、青、紅椒及魚片，盛起待用。
4. 下油兩湯匙爆香肉絲，放入烏冬麵及調味料炒勻，加入洋葱、青、紅椒、魚片及蛋絲，炒至汁收乾上碟，洒上白芝蔴即成。

Ingredients:

2 packets Japanese noodles
1 Japanese fish fillet
1/2 onion
1 green pepper
1 red chilli
4 oz shredded pork
2 eggs
1 tbsp fried white sesame seeds

Marinade:

2 tsp light soy sauce
1/4 tsp sugar
1/2 tsp cornflour
1 tbsp oil

Seasoning for eggs:

1/4 tsp salt
pepper
1/2 tsp cornflour
1 tbsp water

Seasoning for noodles:

1/4 tsp salt
1/4 tsp sugar
2 tsp light soy sauce
1 tbsp ginger sauce
sesame oil
pepper
3 tbsp water

Method:

1. Slice fish fillet. Shred onion, green pepper and red chilli.
2. Marinate pork. Mix egg with seasoning. Fry to form omelette and shred.
3. Make noodles loose. Saute onion, green pepper, red chilli and fish fillet with 2 tbsp oil. Dish up and set aside.
4. Saute pork with 2 tbsp oil. Add noodles and seasoning. Mix well. Put in onion, green pepper, red chilli, fish fillet and egg. Fry until sauce has dried up. Dish up. Sprinkle with white sesame seeds. Serve.

鮮茄牛肉菠菜麵
SPINACH NOODLES WITH TOMATOES AND BEEF

正宗的菠菜麵製法，是在製麵材料中加入菠菜茸，如此不單令麵條更可口，同時營養更加豐富。

材料：

菠菜麵	四個
細番茄	八個
牛肉	四兩
蒜茸	一茶匙

調味料：

生抽	兩茶匙
糖	1/8 茶匙
生粉	一茶匙
清水、油	各一湯匙

獻汁料：

茄汁	三湯匙
鹽	半茶匙
糖	一湯匙
生粉	1 1/2 茶匙
清水	3/4 杯
麻油、胡椒粉	少許

做法：

1. 菠菜麵放入滾水內灼熟，盛乾水份上碟。
2. 番茄洗淨，抹乾水待用。
3. 牛肉切片，加調味料拌勻，泡嫩油，取出盛乾油份。
4. 下油兩湯匙爆香蒜茸，下獻汁料煮滾，放入牛肉、番茄兜勻，淋在菠菜麵上即成。

Ingredients:
4 spinach noodles
8 small tomatoes
5 oz beef
1 tsp crushed garlic

Seasoning:
2 tsp light soy sauce
1/8 tsp sugar
1 tsp cornflour
1 tbsp water
1 tbsp oil

Sauce:
3 tbsp tomato ketchup
1/2 tsp salt
1 tbsp sugar
1 $\frac{1}{2}$ tsp cornflour
$\frac{3}{4}$ cup water
sesame oil
pepper

Method:
1. Cook noodles in boiling water. Dish up on serving plate.
2. Wash and pat dry tomatoes. Set aside.
3. Shred beef. Mix with seasoning and saute in warm oil. Drain.
4. Saute garlic with 2 tbsp oil. Add sauce and bring to the boil. Mix in beef and tomatoes. Pour over spinach noodles. Serve.

斑球伊麵

E-FU NOODLES WITH GAROUPA

伊麵是用油炸成的，放置的時間過久，便會發出油「益」味，煮時可在滾水中加少許醋，盛起過冷河，異味便會消失。

材料：

石斑肉、芥蘭	各八兩
伊麵	兩個
紅蘿蔔花	數片

醃料：

鹽	¼茶匙
蛋白、油	各一湯匙
胡椒粉	少許
生粉	一茶匙

湯料：

上湯	一杯
清水	半杯
生抽	一茶匙
鹽、糖	各¼茶匙
麻油、胡椒粉	少許

做法：

1. 石斑肉洗淨，吸乾水份切厚片，加醃料醃十五分鐘，泡油至熟，取出瀝乾油份。
2. 伊麵放入滾水內灼軟，取出盛乾。
3. 煮滾湯料，放入伊麵、斑球及紅蘿蔔花煮三分鐘盛起。
4. 芥蘭切段，用鹽、油、水灼熟，放於麵上即成。

Ingredients:

10 oz garoupa fillet
10 oz broccoli
2 big E-Fu noodles
carrot slices

Marinade:

1/4 tsp salt
1 tbsp egg white
1 tbsp oil
pepper
1 tsp cornflour

Soup ingredients:

1 cup stock
1/2 cup water
1 tsp light soy sauce
1/4 tsp salt
1/4 tsp sugar
sesame oil
pepper

Method:

1. Wash, pat dry and thickly shred garoupa. Marinate for 15 minutes. Fry in moderate hot oil until cooked. Drain well.
2. Blanch noodles in boiling water until soft. Drain.
3. Parboil noodles, garoupa fillet and carrot in boiled soup ingredients for 3 minutes. Dish up.
4. Section broccoli. Cook in boiling water together with salt and oil. Pour onto noodles. Serve.

豬扒湯麵

NOODLES WITH PORK CHOPS IN SOUP

上海幼麵味清，是煮湯麵的理想材料，配上香脆的豬扒，在不想吃飯時，不妨做一碗來吃，轉轉口味。

材料：

上海幼麵	八両
豬扒	四塊
葱花	一湯匙

醃料：

鹽、糖	各¼茶匙
酒	一茶匙
生抽	兩茶匙
雞蛋	半隻
生粉	一湯匙

湯料：

上湯	三杯
鹽	¼茶匙
麻油、胡椒粉	少許

做法：

1. 上海幼麵放入滾水內煮熟，取出盛乾水份，用少許油拌勻，放在大碗內。
2. 豬扒剁鬆，加醃料醃三十分鐘，放入滾油中炸至熟及呈金黃色，盛起放在麵上。
3. 把湯料煮滾，淋在豬扒上，洒上葱花即成。

Ingredients:
10 oz Shanghai noodles
4 pork chops
1 tbsp chopped spring onion

Marinade:
1/4 tsp salt
1/4 tsp sugar
1 tsp wine
2 tsp light soy sauce
1/2 egg
1 tbsp cornflour

Soup ingredients:
3 cups stock
1/4 tsp salt
sesame oil
pepper

Method:
1. Cook noodles in boiling water. Drain. Mix with pinch of oil and place in a large bowl.
2. Press pork chop with back of chopper. Marinate for 30 minutes. Then fry in hot oil until cooked and slightly brown. Place on noodles.
3. Boil soup ingredients and pour onto pork chops. Sprinkle with spring onion. Serve.

雙鮮烏冬麵

JAPANESE NOODLES WITH SEAFOOD IN SOUP

烏冬既爽口，又易煮，只需花很少時間便可以弄好，所以即使趕時間也無礙，這裏介紹的一款「雙鮮烏冬麵」，實為不錯的選擇。

材料：
烏冬麵	兩包
中蝦	四隻
蟹柳	四條
菜心	四兩

醃料：
鹽	⅛茶匙
麻油、胡椒粉	少許

湯料：
上湯	一杯
清水	1½杯
糖、鹽	各¼茶匙
胡椒粉	少許

做法：

1. 中蝦去殼去腸，保留蝦尾，洗淨吸乾水份，切雙飛，加醃料拌勻。

2. 煮滾湯料，放入烏冬麵煮至再滾，將蝦及蟹柳放在面上，加蓋煮約三分鐘。

3. 菜心用鹽、油、水灼熟，盛起放於麵上即可進食。

Ingredients:
2 packets Japanese noodles
4 medium-sized shrimps
4 crab fillets
5 oz choi-sum vegetable

Marinade:
$\frac{1}{8}$ tsp salt
sesame oil
pepper

Soup ingredients:
1 cup stock
1 $\frac{1}{2}$ cups water
$\frac{1}{4}$ tsp sugar
$\frac{1}{4}$ tsp salt
pepper

Method:
1. Shell, devein and wash shrimps. Pat dry and slit in middle but don't sever. Mix with marinade.
2. Boil soup ingredients. Add noodles and bring to the boil. Put shrimps and crab fillets on top. Cover and cook for about 3 minutes.
3. Cook vegetable in water together with salt and oil. Place on noodles. Serve hot.

上海炒粗麵

SHANGHAI-STYLE FRIED FLAT NOODLES

　　上海粗炒所用的麵爲最粗的上海麵，因麵條粗的關係，會比較難入味，所以炒之前一定要煮到熟透，再用凍水冲去膠質，然後晾乾水來炒才會入味，若麵條未熟透，便不入味。

材料：

上海粗麵、椰菜	各八両
瘦肉	四両

醃料：

老抽、生抽、生粉	各半茶匙
油	一湯匙

調味料：

老抽	一湯匙
鹽	半茶匙
糖	¼茶匙
麻油、胡椒粉	少許
清水	四湯匙

做法：

1. 上海粗麵放入滾水內煮五分鐘，取出冲凍水，盛乾水份待用。
2. 瘦肉切絲，加醃料拌勻。
3. 燒熱兩湯匙油，放入肉絲炒熟盛起。
4. 椰菜洗淨切絲，下油兩湯匙炒至軟身盛起。
5. 燒熱油兩湯匙，放入上海粗麵及調味料炒至水份收乾，加入肉絲、椰菜炒勻即可上碟。

Ingredients:
10 oz Shanghai flat noodles
10 oz cabbage
5 oz lean pork

Marinade:
1/2 tsp dark soy sauce
1/2 tsp light soy sauce
1/2 tsp cornflour
1 tbsp oil

Seasoning:
1 tbsp dark soy sauce
1/2 tsp salt
1/4 tsp sugar
sesame oil
pepper
4 tbsp water

Method:
1. Parboil noodles for 5 minutes. Remove and rinse in cold water. Drain and set aside.
2. Shred pork. Mix with marinade.
3. Fry pork with 2 tbsp oil until cooked. Dish up.
4. Wash and shred cabbage. Fry with 2 tbsp oil until soft. Dish up.
5. Heat 2 tbsp oil. Put in noodles and seasoning. Fry to remove excess water. Add pork and cabbage. Mix well and dish up. Serve.

熟，吃時不用再煮，但爲了衛生起見，買回來時最好用凍開水沖洗一下，因麵條表面很肥膩，易吸塵之故。吃冷麵時加點醋，既可殺菌，更可刺激食慾。

材料：

冷麵	半斤
火腿絲、青瓜絲、	
紅蘿蔔絲	各三湯匙
雞胸肉	三両
白芝麻（炒香）	一湯匙

雞肉調味料：

鹽	¼茶匙
生粉	半茶匙
胡椒粉	少許
油	一湯匙

醃料：

洋醋、糖	各兩茶匙

麵調味料：

芝麻醬、生抽、糖	各一湯匙
辣椒油、浙醋	各一茶匙

做法：

1. 雞胸肉切絲，加調味料拌勻，放入滾水內飛水至熟，取出瀝乾水份。
2. 青瓜絲、紅蘿蔔絲加醃料醃一小時，搾乾水份。
3. 冷麵放在碟上，加調味料拌勻，放上火腿絲、雞絲、青瓜絲及紅蘿蔔絲，再洒上白芝麻即成。

Ingredients:

3/4 lb cool noodles
3 tbsp shredded ham
3 tbsp shredded cucumber
3 tbsp shredded carrot
4 oz chicken breast meat
1 tbsp fried white sesame seeds

Seasoning for chicken breast meat:

1/4 tsp salt
1/2 tsp cornflour
pepper
1 tbsp oil

Marinade:

2 tsp white vinegar
2 tsp sugar

Seasoning for noodles:

1 tbsp sesame paste
1 tbsp light soy sauce
1 tbsp sugar
1 tsp chilli oil
1 tsp red vinegar

Method:

1. Shred and mix chicken breast meat with seasoning. Cook in boiling water. Remove and drain.
2. Marinate cucumber and carrot for 1 hour. Squeeze out excess water.
3. Place noodles on serving dish. Mix well with seasoning. Top with ham, chicken meat, cucumber and carrot. Sprinkle with white sesame seeds. Serve.

雜錦煲仔麵

ASSORTED NOODLES IN POT

「煲仔飯」或「煲仔菜」大家吃得多，不妨試試做一個「煲仔麵」來吃。
這款煲仔麵用料既多，做出來的效果是色香味全，兼營養豐富，實為不
錯的介紹。

材料：

蝦子麵	四個
中蝦	四隻
雞蛋	兩隻
冬菇	六隻
芥菜胆	四兩

調味料：

糖、油	各一茶匙

湯料：

清水	三杯
鹽、糖	各¼茶匙
麻油、胡椒粉	少許

做法：

1. 蝦子麵放入滾水內灼熟，取出盛乾水份，放入煲仔內。
2. 雞蛋原隻煲熟，去殼切片。
3. 冬菇浸軟去蒂，加入調味料拌勻，隔水蒸十分鐘。
4. 芥菜胆用鹽、油、水灼熟盛起。
5. 中蝦連殼洗淨。煮滾湯料，放入中蝦煮四分鐘，把中蝦、雞蛋、冬菇及芥菜胆排放在蝦子麵上，淋上滾湯即可上桌。

Ingredients:

4 shrimp-roe noodles
4 medium-sized shrimps
2 eggs
6 dried black mushrooms
5 oz mustard tubers

Seasoning:

1 tsp sugar
1 tsp oil

Soup ingredients:

3 cups water
1/4 tsp salt
1/4 tsp sugar
sesame oil
pepper

Method:

1. Cook noodles in boiling water. Drain well and place in earthen-pot.
2. Poach eggs. Shell and slice.
3. Soak and trim mushrooms. Mix with seasoning. Then steam for 10 minutes.
4. Blanch mustard tubers in boiling water together with salt and oil until cooked. Dish up.
5. Wash shrimps. Simmer in boiled soup ingredients for 4 minutes. Arrange shrimps, eggs, mushrooms and mustard tubers neatly on noodles. Pour boiled soup on top. Serve.

火腿蘑菇焗闊條麵

FETTUCCINE WITH HAM AND MUSHROOMS

意大利粉麵早已成為西菜中的一個獨立部份，其種類不下十多種，闊條麵亦為其中一種。依照意大利人世代相傳的廚藝心得，烹調時配上忌廉及蘑菇醬汁，特別好吃。

材料：

意大利闊條麵	半磅
忌廉雞湯	一罐
蘑菇	四安士
火腿	三安士
芝士、黑椒碎	少許
蒜茸	一茶匙

調味料：

鹽	半茶匙
胡椒粉	少許

做法：

1. 闊條麵放入熱水中煮至軟身，用凍水冲淨，瀝乾待用。
2. 蘑菇切片，火腿切粗條，芝士刨碎待用。
3. 忌廉雞湯用一杯清水拌勻，待用。
4. 下油兩湯匙爆香蒜茸，放入闊條麵及調味料炒勻上碟，放入一半雞湯及蘑菇、火腿，將其餘雞湯淋在上面，洒上芝士碎及黑椒碎。
5. 將碟放入焗爐，焗十五分鐘或至表面呈金黃色即可取出進食。

Ingredients:

$\frac{1}{2}$ lb Italian fettuccine
1 can cream of chicken
4 oz button mushrooms
3 oz ham
cheese
finely ground black pepper
1 tsp crushed garlic

Seasoning:

$\frac{1}{2}$ tsp salt
pepper

Method:

1. Parboil fettuccine until soft. Remove and rinse in cold water. Drain well.
2. Shred button mushrooms. Thickly strip ham. Grate cheese and set aside.
3. Blend cream of chicken in 1 cup water. Set aside.
4. Saute garlic with 2 tbsp oil. Add fettuccine and seasoning. Mix well and dish up. Mix $\frac{1}{2}$ can cream of chicken, button mushrooms and ham with fettuccine. Pour rest of chicken cream on top. Sprinkle with cheese and black pepper.
5. Bake well-prepared fettuccine in oven for 15 minutes or bake until slightly brown. Remove and serve.

鮮蝦雲吞麵

NOODLES WITH FRESH SHRIMP WONTON IN SOUP

包雲吞是十分講技巧的，除了餡料不可放得太多之外，可加些少蛋液在埋口部份，因蛋液有黏性，雲吞皮便不易散開。

材料：

蝦子麵	四個
雲吞皮、鮮蝦仁	各四両
瘦肉	三両
雞蛋	一隻
韮黃	一両

醃料：

鹽	半茶匙
生粉	一湯匙
麻油、胡椒粉	少許

湯料：

上湯	五杯
生抽	一湯匙
鹽	$\frac{1}{4}$茶匙
胡椒粉	少許

做法：

1. 蝦子麵放入滾水內灼熟，取出盛碗內。
2. 韮黃洗淨切段，雞蛋打散。
3. 鮮蝦仁洗淨，吸乾水份。瘦肉剁碎，加入醃料及蛋液兩湯匙拌勻成餡料。
4. 每件雲吞皮放入適量餡料，包成雲吞，放入滾水內煮至浮起，再煮半分鐘至熟，取出放在麵上，洒上韮黃。
5. 煮滾湯料，淋在雲吞麵上即成。

Ingredients:
4 shrimp-roe noodles
5 oz wonton skin
5 oz fresh shrimps (shells removed)
4 oz lean pork
1 egg
1 $\frac{1}{3}$ oz yellow chives

Marinade:
$\frac{1}{2}$ tsp salt
1 tbsp cornflour
sesame oil
pepper

Soup ingredients:
5 cups stock
1 tbsp light soy sauce
$\frac{1}{4}$ tsp salt
pepper

Method:
1. Cook noodles in boiling water. Dish up in bowl.
2. Wash and section yellow chives. Beat egg.
3. Wash and pat dry shrimps. Mince pork. Mix the above ingredients with marinade and 2 tbsp beaten egg to make fillings.
4. Wrap each wonton skin with suitable amount of fillings. Parboil wontons until all float. Simmer for another $\frac{1}{2}$ minute until cooked. Pour onto noodles. Sprinkle with yellow chives.
5. Boil soup ingredients. Pour over noodles. Serve.

麵

WITH ROAST CHICKEN SLICES

差不多,同樣是要多汁,能被麵吸收才能入味,
條與材料一齊炆煮,辦麵是先將麵條煨熟,再將

材料：	
粗蛋麵	六両
燒雞脾、紅椒	各一隻
薑絲	兩湯匙
蔥	四棵

調味料：

蠔油、生抽	各兩湯匙
糖	¼茶匙
麻油、胡椒粉	少許
清水	半杯

做法：

1. 麵放入滾水中挑散,取出沖凍水。
2. 燒雞脾起肉切絲。
3. 紅椒、蔥切絲。
4. 燒熱油四湯匙爆香薑絲,下調味料煮滾,放入粗麵煮至汁將收乾,加入燒雞、紅椒及蔥絲炒勻上碟即成。

Ingredients:

8 oz egg noodles (flat)
1 roast chicken thigh
1 red chilli
2 tbsp shredded ginger
4 sprigs spring onion

Seasoning:

2 tbsp oyster sauce
2 tbsp light soy sauce
1/4 tsp sugar
sesame oil
pepper
½ cup water

Method:

1. Blanch noodles in boiling water and make them loose. Take out and rinse in cold water.
2. Remove bones from chicken thigh and cut into slices.
3. Shred red chilli and spring onions.
4. Saute ginger with 4 tbsp oil. Add seasoning and cook. Put in noodles and braise until sauce has nearly dried up. Mix in chicken slices, red chilli and spring onions. Blend well and dish up. Serve.

鮮蝦炒紅米飯
FRIED RED RICE WITH SHRIMPS

紅米價格便宜，營養成分又高，應多多利用來作主食。紅米因含有大量鉄質，對貧血之人，具有增血的功能。

材料：

紅米	六両
蝦仁	四両
酸菜梗粒、芥蘭梗粒	各兩湯匙
雞蛋	兩隻
五香豆腐	一件
清水	1½杯

醃料：

鹽	¼茶匙
生粉	半茶匙
胡椒粉	少許

蛋調味料：

鹽	¼茶匙
酒、生粉	各一茶匙
清水	一湯匙

飯調味料：

鹽	半茶匙
麻油	少許

做法：

1. 蝦仁洗淨吸乾水份，加入醃料拌勻，泡油取出，盛乾油份。
2. 雞蛋打散，加入調味料拌勻，煎成蛋皮後切粗粒。
3. 五香豆腐用滾水冲洗，切粗粒。
4. 紅米洗淨，加水煮成飯，取出吹凍。
5. 下油兩湯匙爆炒芥蘭，酸菜、五香豆腐及蝦仁至熟盛起。
6. 燒熱油兩湯匙，放入紅米飯及調味料炒熱，加入上項材料及雞蛋炒勻即可上碟。

Ingredients:
8 oz red rice
5 oz shrimps (shells removed)
2 tbsp diced preserved mustard stem
2 tbsp diced broccoli stem
2 eggs
1 spicy beancurd
1 ½ cups water

Marinade:
¼ tsp salt
½ tsp cornflour
pepper

Seasoning for eggs:
¼ tsp salt
1 tsp wine
1 tsp cornflour
1 tbsp water

Seasoning for rice:
½ tsp salt
sesame oil

Method:
1. Wash and pat dry shrimps. Mix with marinade. Saute, remove and drain.
2. Beat eggs. Mix with seasoning. Fry to form omelette and cut into cubes.
3. Rinse beancurd in hot water and cut into cubes.
4. Wash and cook rice in water. Remove and cool down.
5. Add 2 tbsp oil. Saute broccoli, preserved mustard, beancurd and shrimps. Fry until cooked. Dish up.
6. Heat 2 tbsp oil. Fry rice together with seasoning until heated. Add in the above ingredients and eggs. Mix well and dish up. Serve.

黃鱔焗糙米飯
BRAISED COARSE RICE WITH YELLOW EEL

　　糙米是一種營養價值相當高的食物，和精白米相比較，其維他命 B$_1$、B$_2$高出四倍以上，故自古即爲治療腳氣病的良好食物。而黃鱔是魚類中含維他命 A 最豐富的，有補中益血、通經絡的功能，對女性貧血或老年人的血衰都很有功用。

材料：

糙米	六両
黃鱔	一斤
冬菇	四隻
芫茜、葱	各兩棵
鹽	一茶匙
油	兩茶匙
清水	1½杯

醃料：

生抽	兩茶匙
生粉、薑汁、酒	各一茶匙

調味料：

糖	半茶匙
油	一茶匙

做法：

1. 黃鱔洗淨，放入滾水內飛水，取出沖凍水去潺，吸乾水份切段，加入醃料拌勻待用。
2. 冬菇浸軟去蒂，切條加調味料拌勻。
3. 芫茜、葱切粒。
4. 糙米洗淨，加入鹽、油、水煮至起飯眼，加入黃鱔及冬菇，改慢火焗約十分鐘，食時洒上芫茜、葱拌勻即成。

Ingredients:
8 oz coarse rice
1 ⅓ lb yellow eel
4 dried black mushrooms
2 sprigs parsley
2 sprigs spring onions
1 tsp salt
2 tsp oil
1 ½ cups water

Marinade:
2 tsp light soy sauce
1 tsp cornflour
1 tsp ginger sauce
1 tsp wine

Seasoning:
1/2 tsp sugar
1 tsp oil

Method:
1. Wash, parboil and drain fish. Rinse in cold water to remove sticky substance. Pat dry, section and marinate. Set aside.
2. Soak and trim mushrooms. Strip and mix with seasoning.
3. Dice parsley and spring onions.
4. Wash and cook rice in water together with salt and oil. When it has just boiled up, put in fish and mushrooms. Braise over low heat for about 10 minutes. Sprinkle with parsley and spring onions. Serve.

香茜荷葉飯

STEAMED RICE WITH PARSLEY WRAPPED IN LOTUS LEAF

做荷葉飯當然以新鮮荷葉最理想。如買不到新鮮荷葉，亦可在雜貨舖買乾的。荷葉買回來後，一定要用滾水浸洗，既去塵，又令葉身變軟，然後用凍水再洗。包飯時先在葉上掃一層油，使葉面有光亮的感覺，同時使材料不會黏在葉上。

材料：

白飯	三碗
蝦仁、雞肉	各三兩
章魚、叉燒	各二兩
冬菇	四隻
雞蛋	一隻
荷葉	兩張
芫茜	兩棵

醃料：

生抽	兩茶匙
生粉	半茶匙
油	一湯匙

調味料：

生抽	兩茶匙
鹽	¼茶匙
麻油、胡椒粉	少許

做法：

1. 蝦仁洗淨，吸乾水份，泡油待用。
2. 章魚、冬菇浸軟洗淨，隔水蒸十分鐘，取出切粒。
3. 雞蛋打散，煎成蛋皮後切粒。
4. 雞肉切粒，加醃料拌勻，泡油待用。叉燒切粒，芫茜洗淨切段。
5. 荷葉放入滾水內拖軟，取出抹乾，掃油，將所有材料與白飯混合，加入調味料拌勻，放在荷葉上包好，隔水蒸三十分鐘取出即可進食。

Ingredients:
3 bowls plain rice
4 oz shrimps (shells removed)
4 oz chicken meat
3 oz octopus
3 oz barbecued pork
4 dried black mushrooms
1 egg
2 sheets lotus leaves
2 sprigs parsley

Marinade:
2 tsp light soy sauce
1/2 tsp cornflour
1 tbsp oil

Seasoning:
2 tsp light soy sauce
1/4 tsp salt
sesame oil
pepper

Method:
1. Wash and pat dry shrimps. Saute and set aside.
2. Soak octopus and mushrooms. Wash. Steam for 10 minutes. Remove and dice.
3. Beat egg. Fry to form omelette and dice.
4. Dice chicken meat. Marinate, saute and set aside. Dice barbecued pork. Wash and section parsley.
5. Scald lotus leave in boiling water until soft. Remove, pat dry and brush oil. Mix ingredients and rice together. Blend with seasoning. Wrap contents with lotus leaves. Steam for 30 minutes. Remove and serve hot.

燒鰻魚飯
RICE WITH BRAISED EEL

　　鰻魚飯是日本料理中很著名的食品。日本人認爲夏天吃鰻魚最好，因爲鰻魚含非常多的維他命 A、D，可以應付夏天體力的消耗。而鰻魚又能治療痔疾、惡瘡、小兒疳疾及小兒夜盲症等。

材料：

鰻魚	十二両
米	六両
清水	1½杯

醃料：

老抽	一湯匙
生抽	一茶匙
糖	⅛茶匙

調味料：

日本甜豉油	兩湯匙
麻油	一茶匙
鹽	半茶匙
胡椒粉	少許

做法：

1. 鰻魚洗淨去骨，吸取水份，加醃料拌勻。
2. 預熱焗爐十五分鐘，放入鰻魚用高火焗十五分鐘至微焦黃色，取出待用。
3. 米洗淨，加水煮成飯，加入調味料拌勻，放上鰻魚即可進食。

Ingredients:
1 lb water eel
8 oz rice
1 ½ cups water
Marinade:
1 tbsp dark soy sauce
1 tsp light soy sauce
⅛ tsp sugar
Seasoning:
2 tbsp Japanese sweet soy
1 tsp sesame oil
½ tsp salt
pepper
Method:
1. Wash fish. Remove bones and pat dry. Mix with marinade.
2. Preheat oven for 15 minutes. Braise fish at high power for 15 minutes until slightly brown. Dish up.
3. Wash and cook rice, then mix with seasoning. Put fish on top. Serve.

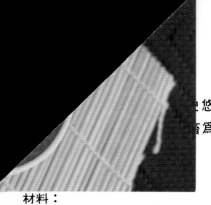

悠久，遠在周□□□□醫學家們就提出
□□爲益、五菜爲充」的膳食製配原則，重視膳

材料：	
中蝦、青口、帶子	各四隻
石斑肉	四両
紅蘿蔔	二両
白飯	三碗
奶油雞湯	半罐
黃薑粉	半茶匙
椰汁	¾杯
淡奶	¼杯
雞蛋	一隻
蒜茸	一茶匙
洋葱	半個

醃料：

鹽	¼茶匙
生粉	半茶匙
胡椒粉	少許
油	一湯匙

做法：

1. 中蝦去殼去腸洗淨，石斑肉切厚件。
2. 中蝦、帶子、青口及石斑肉分別用醃料拌勻，放入滾水中煮熟，取出吸乾水份。
3. 紅蘿蔔、洋葱切粗粒，雞蛋打散。
4. 下油兩湯匙，加入雞蛋及白飯炒熱上碟。
5. 燒熱油兩湯匙炒香洋葱、黃薑粉，加入奶油雞湯煮成濃汁，逐少加入椰汁及淡奶，放入紅蘿蔔煮至滾，最後下中蝦、帶子、青口及石斑肉輕力兜勻，放在飯面。
6. 預熱焗爐十五分鐘，放入海鮮飯，用高火焗二十分鐘至呈金黃色即可取出進食。

Ingredients:
4 medium-sized shrimps
4 mussels
4 scallops
5 oz garoupa fillet
3 oz carrot
3 bowls plain rice
1/2 can creamy chicken soup
1/2 tsp tumeric
3/4 cup coconut juice
1/4 cup evaporated milk
1 egg
1 tsp crushed garlic
1/2 onion

Marinade:
1/4 tsp salt
1/2 tsp cornflour
pepper
1 tbsp oil

Method:
1. Shell, devein and wash shrimps. Thickly shred garoupa.
2. Marinate shrimps,scallops, mussels and garoupa. All blanch in boiling water until cooked. Remove and pat dry.
3. Cut carrot and onion into cubes. Beat egg.
4. Fry egg and rice with 2 tbsp oil until heated. Dish up.
5. Saute onion and tumeric with 2 tbsp oil. Add chicken soup and cook to thickening consistency. Pour in coconut juice and evaporated milk little by little. Stir in carrot. Bring to the boil. Then fold in shrimps, scallops, mussels and garoupa lightly. Pour contents onto rice.
6. Preheat oven for 15 minutes. Bake seafood rice at high power for 20 minutes until slightly brown. Remove and serve.

雪菜肉絲泡飯

SUIT-NEI-HOONG VEGETABLE AND SHREDDED PORK WITH RICE IN SOUP

　　炎夏天時，食慾不振，當你發覺一般白米飯難以下嚥時，不妨試試做一款泡飯，使進食更為容易。這款泡飯用料簡單，做起來絕不困難。

材料：

雪菜、瘦肉	各四兩
蝦米	一湯匙
白飯	四碗

醃料：

生抽	一茶匙
生粉	半茶匙
油	兩茶匙

調味料：

鹽	適量

做法：

1. 雪菜洗淨切粒，蝦米洗淨待用。
2. 瘦肉切絲，加醃料拌勻。
3. 下油半湯匙爆炒雪菜及蝦米。
4. 煮滾三杯水，將雪菜、蝦米、白飯加入煮至滾起，再放入肉絲，煮至熟，下鹽調味即可盛起進食。

Ingredients:
5 oz suit-nei-hoong vegetable
5 oz lean pork
1 tbsp dried shrimps
4 bowls plain rice

Marinade:
1 tsp light soy sauce
1/2 tsp cornflour
2 tsp oil

Seasoning:
salt

Method:
1. Wash and dice vegetable. Wash dried shrimps and set aside.
2. Shred and marinate pork.
3. Saute vegetable and dried shrimps with $\frac{1}{2}$ tbsp oil.
4. Boil 3 cups water. Add vegetable, dried shrimps and rice. Bring to the boil. Put in pork and simmer until cooked. Stir in seasoning. Serve.

生炒咸魚牛肉飯
FRIED RICE WITH SALTED FISH AND BEEF

炒飯雖然比較「熱氣」，但甘香可口，令人食慾大振，這款「生炒咸魚牛肉飯」更是芳香四溢，必令你和家人食指大動。

材料：

咸魚	二両
免治牛肉、椰菜	各四両
葱	三棵
蒜茸、薑粒	各一茶匙
白飯	四碗
上湯	半杯

醃料：

生抽、油	各一湯匙
生粉	一茶匙

做法：

1. 咸魚去皮去骨，切成小粒，用熱油炸至微黃色盛起。
2. 牛肉加醃料拌勻，椰菜切絲，葱切粒。
3. 燒熱一湯匙油炒熟椰菜，取出滴乾油份，再下油一湯匙炒熟牛肉盛起。
4. 燒熱油四湯匙，將飯炒至鬆散，分數次洒下上湯，加入蒜茸、薑粒炒至有香味，再加入咸魚、牛肉及椰菜炒勻，最後加入葱花炒勻即可上碟。

Ingredients:
3 oz salted fish
5 oz minced beef
5 oz cabbage
3 sprigs spring onions
1 tsp crushed garlic
1 tsp diced ginger
4 bowls plain rice
1/2 cup stock

Marinade:
1 tbsp light soy sauce
1 tbsp oil
1 tsp cornflour

Method:
1. Remove skin and bones from salted fish. Dice. Deep fry until slightly brown. Dish up.
2. Marinate beef. Shred cabbage. Dice spring onions.
3. Fry cabbage with 1 tbsp oil until cooked. Remove and drain well. Fry beef with 1 tbsp oil until cooked. Dish up.
4. Heat 4 tbsp oil. Fry rice and make it loose. Sprinkle with stock for several times. Add garlic and ginger. Fry until fragrant. Then stir in salted fish, beef, cabbage and spring onions. Mix well and dish up. Serve.

咖喱雞提子飯

RICE WITH CURRY CHICKEN AND RAISINS

提子乾是造血食品，可以用作炒菜佐餐，在咖喱飯中加入提子乾，不僅美味可口，且有補血的效能，最宜貧血病患者服用。

材料：

白飯	三碗
雞肉	六両
提子乾	三湯匙
乾葱茸、咖喱粉	各兩茶匙
紅蘿蔔	二両

醃料：

生抽	兩茶匙
生粉	半茶匙
油	一湯匙

調味料：

生抽	一茶匙
鹽	半茶匙

做法：

1. 雞肉切小件，加醃料拌勻。
2. 紅蘿蔔去皮切條。
3. 下油三湯匙爆香乾葱茸及咖喱粉，加入雞件炒至熟盛起。
4. 下油一湯匙，倒入白飯、紅蘿蔔炒至熱，雞件回鑊，加入提子乾兜勻即可上桌。

Ingredients:
3 bowls plain rice
8 oz chicken meat
3 tbsp raisins
2 tsp crushed shallot
2 tsp curry powder
3 oz carrot

Marinade:
2 tsp light soy sauce
1/2 tsp cornflour
1 tbsp oil

Seasoning:
1 tsp light soy sauce
1/2 tsp salt

Method:
1. Cut chicken meat into small pieces and marinate.
2. Skin and strip carrot.
3. Saute shallot and curry powder with 3 tbsp oil. Add chicken meat and fry until cooked. Dish up.
4. Fry rice and carrot with 1 tbsp oil until heated. Return chicken meat. Mix in raisins. Serve.

臘味糯米飯

GLUTINOUS RICE WITH DRIED PORK AND LIVER SAUSAGES

糯米本身有滋養、養氣及充胃的功效。不過，糯米吃下後，停留在胃中的時間較長，故吃得過多會引致消化不良，宜加注意。

材料：

糯米	八両
潤腸、臘腸	各兩條
蝦米	一両
花生	二両
芫茜	兩棵
葱	一棵

調味料：

生抽	四湯匙
老抽	兩湯匙
糖	一湯匙
麻油	兩茶匙

做法：

1. 糯米洗淨，用浸過米面清水浸四小時，盛乾水分，放入高身的碟內。
2. 臘腸、潤腸用滾水沖洗乾淨，放在糯米上，隔水大火蒸三十分鐘，取出臘腸、潤腸切粒。
3. 蝦米洗淨，下油一湯匙爆香，加入調味料慢火煮至糖溶，放入糯米飯、臘腸炒勻上碟。
4. 花生炸脆，芫茜、葱切粒，洒在糯米飯上即成。

Ingredients:
10 oz glutinous rice
2 dried liver sausages
2 dried pork sausages
1 $\frac{1}{3}$ oz dried shrimps
3 oz peanuts
2 sprigs parsley
1 sprig spring onion

Seasoning:
4 tbsp light soy sauce
2 tbsp dark soy sauce
1 tbsp sugar
2 tsp sesame oil

Method:

1. Wash and soak glutinous rice for 4 hours (Water should be sufficient enough to cover the rice). Drain well. Place in a deep plate.
2. Rinse sausages in hot water, then put onto glutinous rice. Steam over high heat for 30 minutes. Remove sausages and dice.
3. Saute dried shrimps with 1 tbsp oil. Add seasoning. Cook over low heat until sugar has dissolved. Put in glutinous rice and sausages. Mix well and dish up.
4. Crisp fried peanuts. Dice parsley and spring onion. Sprinkle on glutinous rice. Serve.

鴛鴦炒飯
FRIED RICE IN TWO COLOURS

這款「鴛鴦炒飯」和我們平時所吃的有所不同，是用白米飯與黑糯米飯一起炒。黑糯米要先用水浸四小時，隔乾水份後，隔水蒸熟，然後挑散成一粒粒米粒，炒時才不會黏在一塊。

材料：
黑糯米飯	一碗
白飯	兩碗
青豆	二両
蝦仁	四両
甘筍粒	一湯匙
雞蛋	一隻
葱	兩棵

醃料：
鹽	¼茶匙
胡椒粉	少許
生粉	半茶匙

調味料：
鹽	半茶匙
麻油	少許

做法：
1. 黑糯米洗淨，用浸過米面清水浸四小時，盛乾水份，隔水蒸熟待用。
2. 青豆飛水，蝦仁加醃料拌勻，泡油。
3. 雞蛋煎成蛋皮後切條，葱切粒。
4. 下油兩湯匙炒勻黑糯米飯及白飯，加入青豆、蝦仁、紅蘿蔔、雞蛋及調味料炒至熱，洒上葱粒上碟即成。

Ingredients:
1 bowl black glutinous rice
2 bowls plain rice
3 oz green peas
5 oz shrimps (shells removed)
1 tbsp diced carrot
1 egg
2 sprigs spring onions

Marinade:
¼ tsp salt
pepper
½ tsp cornflour

Seasoning:
½ tsp salt
sesame oil

Method:
1. Wash and soak black glutinous rice for 4 hours (Water should be sufficient enough to cover the rice). Drain well. Steam until cooked. Set aside.
2. Drain green peas. Marinate shrimps and saute.
3. Fry egg to form omelette. Strip. Dice spring onions.
4. Fry black glutinous rice and plain rice with 2 tbsp oil. Mix well. Add green peas, shrimps, carrot, egg and seasoning. Fry until heated. Sprinkle with spring onions. Dish up and serve.

章魚蠔豉煲仔飯

RICE WITH OCTOPUS AND DRIED OYSTERS IN EARTHEN POT

章魚含有大量的蛋白和鈣質，因此胃酸過多者，非常適宜食用章魚，而且其卡路里含量少，吃之不易發胖。

材料：

米	六兩
章魚、蠔豉	各二兩
冬菇	六隻
薑	兩片
葱花	兩湯匙
油	半湯匙
鹽	半茶匙
清水	1¼杯

調味料：

生抽	兩湯匙
糖	¼茶匙
酒、麻油	各一茶匙
胡椒粉	少許

做法：

1. 章魚用清水浸軟，洗淨切粗粒。
2. 蠔豉浸軟洗淨，放入大碗內，倒入滾水，加蓋焗半小時，取出切粒。
3. 冬菇浸軟去蒂，切粒。
4. 下油兩湯匙爆香薑片，放入章魚、蠔豉、冬菇及調味料炒至有香味，盛起待用。
5. 米洗淨，加入油、鹽，拌勻，再放入水煮成飯，將炒熟之材料放在飯面，改文火焗至發出香味，取出薑片不要，食時洒上葱花即成。

Ingredients:
8 oz rice
3 oz octopus
3 oz dried oysters
6 dried black mushrooms
2 slices ginger
2 tbsp finely chopped spring onion
½ tbsp oil
½ tsp salt
1 ¼ cups water

Seasoning:
2 tbsp light soy sauce
¼ tsp sugar
1 tsp wine
1 tsp sesame oil
pepper

Method:
1. Soak, wash and cut octopus into cubes.
2. Soak and wash dried oysters. Place in a large bowl. Pour in boiling water. Cover and bake for ½ hour. Take out and dice.
3. Soak and trim mushrooms. Dice.
4. Saute ginger with 2 tbsp oil. Add octopus, dried oysters, mushrooms and seasoning. Fry until fragrant. Dish up and set aside.
5. Wash and mix rice with oil and salt. Cook with water in pot. Pour well-prepared contents onto rice. Bake over mild heat until fragrant. Dispose ginger. Sprinkle with spring onion. Serve.

田雞焗飯

BRAISED RICE WITH FROGS

　　田雞有清熱治痔，殺虫解毒之功能，此外，田雞所含的脂肪少，蛋白質卻很多，對發育中的小孩或消瘦的小孩是很有益的食品，用田雞來焗飯，芳香味美，可增進食慾。

材料：

田雞	一斤
多菇	六隻
米	六両
葱絲、薑絲	各一湯匙
油	半湯匙
鹽	半茶匙
清水	1¼杯

醃料：

生抽、薑汁	各一湯匙
生粉	一茶匙
油	兩湯匙

多菇醃料：

糖、油	各一茶匙

調味料：

生抽	兩茶匙
老抽	一湯匙
糖	半茶匙

做法：

1. 田雞去內臟洗淨，斬件，加醃料拌勻待用。
2. 多菇浸軟去蒂，加醃料拌勻。
3. 米洗淨放入煲內，加油、鹽拌勻，倒入清水煮至飯滾，加入薑絲、田雞及多菇，改慢火焗至飯及田雞熟，加入調味料拌勻，再洒上葱絲即可進食。

Ingredients:

1 ⅓ lb frogs
6 dried black mushrooms
8 oz rice
1 tbsp shredded spring onion
1 tbsp shredded ginger
½ tbsp oil
½ tsp salt
1 ¼ cups water

Marinade:

1 tbsp light soy sauce
1 tbsp ginger sauce
1 tsp cornflour
2 tbsp oil

Marinade for dried black mushrooms:

1 tsp sugar
1 tsp oil

Seasoning:

2 tsp light soy sauce
1 tbsp dark soy sauce
½ tsp sugar

Method:

1. Remove entrails from frogs. Wash, chop up and marinate. Set aside.
2. Soak, trim and marinate mushrooms.
3. Wash and place rice in pot. Add oil and salt. Mix well. Pour in water and bring to the boil. Add ginger, frogs and mushrooms. Then braise over low heat until rice and frogs are cooked. Blend in seasoning. Sprinkle with spring onion. Serve.

瑤柱排骨煲仔飯

RICE WITH CONPOYS AND SPARERIBS IN EARTHEN POT

煮煲仔飯一定要有耐性，將米放下水中後，要先用猛火煲炊，然後收慢火來慢慢焗，才可令飯既熟透又不會燶。

材料：
米、肉排	各六両
瑤柱	半両
冬菇	五隻
薑絲、油	各一湯匙
葱	三棵
清水	1¼杯

醃料：
蠔油	半湯匙
生抽、生粉	各一茶匙
酒	半茶匙
糖	¼茶匙
油	兩湯匙

調味料：
生抽	¼杯
老抽、糖	各兩湯匙
麻油	兩茶匙

做法：
1. 瑤柱用清水浸軟撕幼。
2. 冬菇浸軟去蒂，切小件；葱洗淨切粒。
3. 肉排斬小件，加入薑絲及醃料拌勻。
4. 拌勻調味料，煮至糖溶盛起。
5. 米洗淨，加入油拌勻，放入煲內加水煲滾，下冬菇、瑤柱、肉排煮至水將收乾，改文火焗至肉排熟透，洒下葱花，加入調味料拌勻即可進食。

Ingredients:
- 8 oz rice
- 8 oz spareribs
- 1 oz conpoys
- 5 dried black mushrooms
- 1 tbsp shredded ginger
- 1 tbsp oil
- 3 sprigs spring onions
- 1¼ cups water

Marinade:
- ½ tbsp oyster sauce
- 1 tsp light soy sauce
- 1 tsp cornflour
- ½ tsp wine
- ¼ tsp sugar
- 2 tbsp oil

Seasoning:
- ¼ cup light soy sauce
- 2 tbsp dark soy sauce
- 2 tbsp sugar
- 2 tsp sesame oil

Method:
1. Soak and tear conpoys into thin shreds.
2. Soak, trim and cut mushrooms into small pieces. Wash and dice spring onions.
3. Chop up spareribs. Mix with ginger and marinade.
4. Mix seasoning ingredients. Cook until sugar has dissolved. Dish up.
5. Wash and mix rice with oil. Place in pot together with water. Bring to the boil. Add mushrooms, conpoys and spareribs. Cook until water has nearly dried up. Then braise over mild heat until spareribs are thoroughly cooked. Sprinkle with spring onions. Add seasoning. Mix well and serve.

菜式豐富 • 味味佳餚 • 海濱食譜 • 實惠享受

保健 • 補療：

合時補療食譜	進補得宜，身體健康
家常補療食譜	補身療病，照顧全家健康
家庭保健食譜	保障家人健康，主婦必讀
兒童健康美食	美食好安排，兒童成長快
孕婦營養食譜	均衡營養，準媽媽之恩物
健康美食譜	低脂肪、低膽固醇，使您遠離疾病
黑色食譜	療養、保健功效大
低膽固醇食譜	口福健康兼而有之
高纖維營養餐單	三餐餸菜款式多，每餐滋味各不同
婦女補療食譜	滋補養顏，強壯身體，抵抗病魔
KEEP FIT 窈窕美容家常菜	KEEP FIT 人士必讀
百類中藥保健食譜	每個家庭必不可缺
百類中藥補療食譜	實用食療手冊家庭必備
驅寒去濕合時蔬菜營養食譜	天氣寒濕，吃後爽利
消暑散熱合時蔬菜營養食譜	炎炎夏日，最宜進食
滋潤解燥合時蔬果營養食譜	天氣乾燥，不可缺少
調臟補益合時蔬菜營養食譜	身體虛弱，最宜進補
百類蔬菜營養食譜	蔬菜營養食法集大成
百類中藥防老食譜	養生健體，延緩衰老

靚湯：

滋潤靚湯	解渴生津，健脾開胃
清燉靚湯	滋潤養陰，補中益氣
明火煲靚湯	清熱解暑，調臟滋補
滋補靚湯	滋陰補腎，清熱解毒，樣樣皆能
常年靚湯	潤燥溫補靚湯，適合四季飲用
解燥老火湯	滋潤解燥，清除熱氣
家常老幼靚湯	適合一家老幼飲用

特色小菜：

潮流美食譜	順應飲食潮流之美食譜
家庭宴客菜	菜式有新意，宴客自奉兩相宜
精裝巧手小菜	一書在手，烹調再無憂
創意味味好餸	美味菜式，為你提供
美味佳餚冠亞季模擬菜式	得獎餸菜，不可小覷
醬料食譜	烹調極易，濃郁冶味
惹味食譜	甜酸苦辣樣樣有，各式餸菜好滋味
營養辣譜	大、中、小辣任君選擇
入廚初哥	教法清楚易明，初哥都變大廚
30分鐘開飯	在職主婦必備工具書
創意食譜	為你炮製創新菜式
節日食譜	中西菜式齊備，烹調方便快捷
節日吉祥食譜與插花	增添喜慶，不可不讀
知慳識儉慳撚手菜	保存營養，經濟衛生
簡速家庭營養食譜	簡易快捷營養高
簡易家常美食	中西菜式齊備，烹調方便快捷
滋味雞譜	美味與健康合而為一
味味好餸	每款餸菜滋味一流
乳酪食譜	健康食品，營養豐富
譚銳佳巧手菜	大師級名廚，得意巧手傑作

風味菜：

懷舊家鄉菜	品嚐鄉土佳餚，重溫昔日口味
各式地方小菜	中國八處地方名菜精選
上海風味家常菜	滙集上海菜之精華
自製壽司	款式千變萬化，製法簡易，滋味無
和味泰國菜	自製泰國食品，品嚐異國風味
家鄉潮州菜	潮州風味菜，令您食指大動
越南菜	包羅越菜精華，餸菜香甜鮮辣

蔬果 • 素菜：

水果美食	色香味全，增添食慾，有益健康
菇類美食	美味可口，營養豐富
蔬果健美食譜	清淡自然，擺脫膩口
低熱量素食	低熱量，色香味全，最適合愛健美
健康素食	促進健康，增加智能，男女老幼皆
素菜譜	延年益壽，健康無憂的食譜精選
鮮果食譜與切雕	鮮果營養與做法面面觀
營養豆品	潤膚養顏功效大

烹調法：

巧手蒸法	不溫不燥，保存餸菜原味
燒烤	室內室外，皆可享受燒烤之樂
南北烹調46法	不同的烹調法，一一為你介紹
砂鍋靚餸	原汁原味，香味四溢
無火煮食	煮食無油煙，主婦樂輕鬆

甜品：

養顏甜品	以水果為主，清甜不膩，滋潤養顏
甜品精點	維持身體所需熱量
低卡路里甜品	味道清甜熱量低，最佳的飯後甜品
滋潤家鄉甜品	集合中國甜品精華

包點飯麵：

美點小食	鹹甜俱備，巧手易做，添情添趣
餃子	傳統美食添上新意，各式餃子任君
粥粉麵飯	正餐雜糧，一爐共冶
自製班戟	揉合傳統與新意，班戟款式多變化

海產系列：

海鮮美食	創製味美海產佳餚
百類海味食譜	海味烹調方法逐一介紹
急凍海產食譜	鮮甜美味，媲美海鮮

巧手三十六計：

燜	三十六種燜法絕招，三十六種新口
煎	點心小菜甘香可口，滋味無窮
炸	點心香脆，小菜可口
蒸	保持小菜、點心原汁原味